the kid's cookbook

a great book for kids who love to cook!

general editor **Chuck Williams**
recipes and text **Abigail Johnson Dodge**
photography **Leigh Beisch**

WELDON OWEN

contents